THE
UNCHOSEN
LAND

Arnica

THE UNCHOSEN LAND

ROBERT INGPEN

RIGBY
OPAL
BOOKS

Books by Robert Ingpen

The Australian Gnomes trilogy

Australian Gnomes
The Voyage of the Poppykettle
The Unchosen Land

Pioneers of Wool
Pioneer Settlement in Australia
Robe: A Portrait of the Past
Marking Time: Australia's Abandoned Buildings
Australia's Heritage Watch

Books illustrated by Robert Ingpen

With Colin Thiele:

Storm Boy
Lincoln's Place
River Murray Mary
Chadwick's Chimney

With Nick Evers:

Paradise and Beyond

With Michael Page:

The Runaway Punt
Turning Points in the Making of Australia
Aussie Battlers (in preparation)

13504

National Library of Australia
Cataloguing-in-Publication entry

Ingpen, Robert, 1936–
    The unchosen land
    ISBN 0 7270 1517 6.
    I. Title.

A823′.3

RIGBY PUBLISHERS LIMITED • ADELAIDE • SYDNEY
MELBOURNE • BRISBANE • PERTH • AUCKLAND
NEW YORK • LONDON
First published 1981
Text and illustrations copyright © 1981 Robert Ingpen
All rights reserved
Colour separations by Colour Scanners Pty Limited, Sydney
Type set in 12 on 15 point Century Schoolbook by
B&D Modgraphic Pty Ltd, Bowden, South Australia
Printed in Hong Kong

CHAPTER ONE

THIS IS A STORY of the Realtime and the Dreamtime. It tells of the Oldshadows who remember back to the dawn of time, of the Lilywhites who came from distant countries and of the Third People who came with them. Sometimes the Third People are called gnomes.

And it is the story of the Hairy Peruvians, who made a great voyage across the Pacific Ocean to Australia in their ship *Poppykettle* exactly 400 years ago. In Realtime their voyage took them four years of hope and hazard, difficulty and danger.

The Hairy Peruvians were members of a community of tiny fishermen who lived by the great ocean. When the Shining Spaniards defeated the rulers of their country, the Noble Incas, the community decided to send explorers to find another and more peaceful land.

Their ship was a clay pot, found in the great mountains of the Andes. They rigged the pot with a sail and gave it the name of *Poppykettle*. They loaded her with sacks of poppyseed, to eat on the voyage and make their favourite poppyseed tea, and with six brass keys for ballast, stolen from the Shining Spaniards.

Seven Hairy Peruvians were chosen to sail the clay pot to the west and find a new home for their people. One of them was the woman Arnica, and she stowed away her baby girl, Areca, among the sacks of poppyseed. So it was that eight set out upon the voyage.

Sometimes the *Poppykettle* sailed with fair winds, but sometimes she only drifted at the mercy of the waves. She was driven onto a lonely island, where the people helped the Hairy Peruvians to start again. After that they ran into a great storm which washed one of them overboard, and almost sank the *Poppykettle*. She was cracked and leaking and they thought that all was lost, but they were rescued by a friendly dolphin. He told them to lash the *Poppykettle* to his head, and set off at a great speed.

They did not know where they were going, and when the dolphin at last tipped the *Poppykettle* onto a beach they did not know where they had arrived. They had reached this new country by chance, and so it was their Unchosen Land. When many years had gone by, and the Lilywhites began to arrive, it was also the Unchosen Land

5

for many of those people. They had not chosen to leave their own homes and sail to a country on the other side of the world.

But all that was in the future when the Seven Hairy Peruvians first looked around at this strange land to which the dolphin had brought them. Four of them were men: Don Avante the leader, and Arrant, Astute, and Aloof. Two of them were women, Arnica and Arnago, and the other was little Areca.

Their faithful *Poppykettle* would sail no more, and so they saved the few remaining sacks of poppyseed and dumped them in the dry sand above the high tide mark. Astute and Arrant waded in the shallow water of the bay, and soon managed to trap an unwary scallop which ventured too close to them. The women lit a fire and began to make scallop stew.

Don Avante decided to bury the six brass keys, the only valuable articles left in the *Poppykettle*, in the low cliff along the beach. He could only carry three at a time, and when he had buried these he wandered a little way inland to see more of the new country.

He made his way from the sandy beach, through a belt of long grass, to the place where the great grey trees began. Their speckled leaves cast a canopy of shade, and although he saw no sign of life he had a sense that unseen watchers were keeping their eyes on him.

The feeling became so strong that it drove him back to join the others on the beach. He forgot about the three keys still in the *Poppykettle*. He and the others rested by the cheerful fire, enjoying the pleasant aroma of the dry leaves which Arnica and Arnago had collected for burning. As they crumbled down to fine blue smoke and grey ash they gave out a haunting scent which the Hairy Peruvians had never known before, and somehow it seemed right for the strange new country.

After a hearty meal of the scallop stew they all joined in singing two songs. One was in praise of the *Poppykettle* which had brought them so far, and the other was for little Areca who would grow up in the Unchosen Land.

After the sun had set and their songs were finished they still sat around the fire, drinking mugs of hot poppyseed tea and talking about the future. Nobody talked about the past because that was a bygone. Hairy Peruvians believe they should keep only those events from the past which will be useful in the future. All that they respect as tradition has been carefully chosen, and nobody could imagine any use, in this new land, for remembrance of the events during their years on the Pacific Ocean. Until sleep finally

8

claimed them they talked about the future and Arnica was encouraged to make just one prediction.

Foretelling the future is very important to Hairy Peruvians. They are a race of very small people who look like humans and they have been granted special powers to compensate for their smallness. Telling the future is one of these powers, and with constant practice a Hairy Peruvian can achieve moments of outstanding accuracy at this art. Arnica was renowned for her reliable predictions, which she introduced with great dramatic flair. She had recently predicted that little Areca would one day inherit her skill.

And so when Arnica made her prediction that night everyone except little Areca, who was already asleep, listened very carefully. She began with her usual mystic chanting to set them all in the right mood, but on that night it was subtly different from ever before. Somehow it seemed to be in tune with the soft dark night silvered by the light of countless glowing stars, and the quiet sigh of the ocean along the beach.

Her chanting ended and they listened, still and silent. She spoke slowly and quietly, since she never repeated a prediction, and said 'Very soon we shall all be laughed away over a carpet of soft needles, to the place where the Wobyang Refugees await us.'

They did not understand her prediction but they knew it would come true. They settled down to sleep, and the sound that awoke them early next morning was certainly laughter. The first rays of the sun danced on the gentle ripples of the bay, but the strange laughter came from the opposite direction, somewhere inland beyond the ridge of grey trees.

The Hairy Peruvians sat silently for a long time, trying to locate the source of the sound. After a while the first laughter was answered by a second laughing call, even further away, and then a third and a fourth voice joined in a chain of laughter reaching far away into unknown territory. It seemed to beckon them into the Unchosen Land.

Don Avante and Arnica conferred together and agreed that the laughter confirmed the first part of her prediction, and that they must follow the path of sound. Quietly, a little afraid, they gathered their possessions together and began to make their way through the long grass towards the sound. Don Avante led them, and each took turns carrying little Areca over the rougher country.

Unfamiliar animals and insects were at work for another day, but they kept clear of the strange band of travellers. Once a fieldmouse stood for a moment, gaping openmouthed at the sight of them as they struggled into a clearing formed by generations of nesting bull ants.

They crossed many such clearings, and at one of them they were approached by a sleepy sentry ant. One of the powers developed by Hairy Peruvians is that of understanding the many languages and dialects of animals and insects, and since the spoken language of ants is very nearly international they were to find the talkative ants to be a valuable source of information.

But this first encounter did not help them very much. The sentry ant was in no mood for conversation. The Hairy Peruvians bombarded him with questions, but he said only 'Please don't walk over our home while the family is sleeping.'

'Still asleep?' Don Avante asked. 'But the sun's been up for a long time.'

'It's cold down there,' the bull ant explained. 'We never get up until the sun has warmed right through our home.'

Don Avante then asked about the strange laughter they had heard, but the sentry was bored with the conversation.

He just said gruffly 'Follow it and see.'

Don Avante

CHAPTER TWO

THEY FOLLOWED THE LAUGHTER all day, and in the afternoon found themselves walking over a vast plain covered with she-oaks. These she-oaks whispered softly to them as they passed between their trunks, and they had shed a mass of needles which formed a soft carpet beneath the feet of the Hairy Peruvians. This natural carpet made a pleasant change from walking through the vicious grasses which grew where there were no trees. Kangaroo grass and wallaby grass had sharp seeds, which caught in the clothes of the wanderers and made them itch.

As they walked over the carpet of needles, Arnago picked up a handful and said 'Another part of Arnica's prediction has come true. It is said we would be laughed away over a carpet of needles.'

They camped that night, and the laughter awoke them again in the morning. For three more days the laughter was like the rainbow's end, which always seems to be just a little way away. But on the fifth day a new laughter took over. It used the same sounds but made them a little differently, and came from a different direction so that they swung in from the coastal she-oak plain towards a range of mountains that rose sharply from the flat country. Afternoon ants told them they were being drawn towards the Realm of the Wobyang.

Arrant, who had just finished a long spell of carrying Areca, carefully questioned these local ants. 'What *is* a Wobyang?' he asked. 'What does it look like? Where does it live? Will it be dangerous to follow the laughter into those mountains?'

The ants seemed a little annoyed by the suggestion that the Wobyang was dangerous, and one of them said 'Anyway, we've heard that the Wobyang is away. Don't be afraid to follow the laughter. It will lead you to "the refugees."'

Late one afternoon, six long days after leaving the *Poppykettle*, they began to climb the mountains. She-oaks grew up the slopes, between rocky granite outcrops, and so they did not have to walk through the patches of angry grass. Watching lizards reported their progress to unseen authorities, and still the laughter rang out ahead of them.

At last, Don Avante spotted the source of the laughter. He saw that it came from a bird, but the others would not believe him until he pointed out the feathered creature with the long beak and loud laugh. It sat in a tall sugar gum, and as they watched it opened its beak and began another chorus beginning with the ritual 'Kook, kook.'

They felt their long march was at an end as they approached the white trunk of the kookaburra tree, and saw before them a beautiful green gully full of ferns and lush grasses. A freshwater stream, running from some hidden place deep within the mountains, fed a gleaming pool in the heart of the gully, and many native birds and animals were gathered around the edge of the pool.

The kookaburra stopped laughing and launched himself from his perch high above this scene. With a sudden rush of wings he passed above the startled travellers, and landed among the other birds and animals. The Hairy Peruvians, looking down on the gathering from their position on the high rim of the gully, were astonished. They could not recognise any of the animals and birds and all but one of them were strange beyond belief. The exception was the pelican. He was similar to their friend Brown Pelican, who had helped them to find the *Poppykettle* four years before. He was a different colour but he spoke the same language, although with a different accent, and he was certainly a welcome sight.

Cautiously the Hairy Peruvians made their way down into the gully, until they stood on the side of the pool opposite to the gathering of animals. They felt safe enough with water between them, although, as Astute pointed out, the animals did not seem aggressive.

He began to talk to them, with the pelican helping with unfamiliar words. Slowly the Hairy Peruvians pieced together the story of the Wobyang, to which was added the terrible tale of the Cunmerrie.

Both the Wobyang and the Cunmerrie were huge birds, somewhat resembling a cross between an owl and an eagle, but instead of feathers they had skin like reptiles. Both creatures had huge appetites and terrible tempers.

The Wobyang lived in these mountains, and was able to watch the wide plains all around them and see any enemy approaching. The Cunmerrie lived far away to the north, in a place guarded by watcher termites in their tall mounds.

The great difference between the two creatures was that the Wobyang ate nothing but fruit, whereas the Cunmerrie devoured the flesh of animals. The Wobyang hated the Cunmerrie, and often

14

had saved the animals of the mountains from his clutches.

Astute said 'Now we can understand! But what we don't understand is why you sent kookaburra to lead us to this gathering.'

Pelican answered 'Wobyang has been away from this mountain for a long time and we don't know where he's gone. We're afraid that Cunmerrie may have killed him, and we dare not go searching for him in northern parts in case Cunmerrie sees us.'

Don Avante said 'And you want us to look for him, eh?'

Pelican nodded his big beak. 'Yes, Cunmerrie will not know who you are, but he knows we are friends of Wobyang. And if you do this for us, we will teach you how to live in your Unchosen Land without starving.'

The wanderers were glad to hear this, because they had not found anything suitable to eat as they crossed the wide land and their provisions were running low. But they did not accept the offer without long discussion, while the animals waited patiently.

Don Avante, Astute, and Aloof all wanted to accept the offer. Arrant was completely against it and nothing would change his mind. Arnago, who rarely spoke, said 'Let's rest awhile in this beautiful place before we decide.'

They asked Arnica to forecast the future, but she became confused and could not help them. She did not want to accept, but thought that little Areca might suffer if food became scarce.

At last Don Avante said 'I am your leader and I will decide. We will rest here for a while, and make new clothing that is more comfortable for us. Our old clothes are stiff and stained with the salt from our long voyage. The animals and insects will give us instructions for our journey, and when everyone is ready we will set out. As for Arrant, he shall come with us, but may leave us whenever he finds a place where he will like to live.'

The animals were very relieved, and to show their gratitude they sent the wallabies to collect the remaining sacks of poppyseed, and other heavy items, from the wreck of the *Poppykettle*.

The travellers soon set up camp in the green gully in the Realm of the Wobyang, and busied themselves in making new clothes with the help and advice of the animals. The trouble with their traditional clothes was that they were designed for fishing and seafaring, and not for wandering over dry plains among angry grasses. They wore bandages wrapped tightly around their arms and legs, and the burrs and sharp seeds caught in these and itched their skins.

16

They devised new clothes altogether, which would be cooler than the tight bandages. Soon all the men had trousers and the women had bloomers, but they tied a piece of the old bandages in a bow beneath each knee. They did this so that they would not forget the old ways, and vowed to continue the habit however much they changed other things in their new home. And soon they found it was a good idea because it prevented seeds from creeping up their legs.

Each night, Arnica chanted her forecasting song as they sat around the fire, and followed this with predictions for the future. Many of her predictions, even though they did not understand them at the time, were to come true.

At last they set out on their great journey. They saw many strange sights and unexplained events, but Arnica often had warned them of these and so they were not afraid. After nine months of travel, Arrant decided to settle down at a place near the junction of two great rivers. They bade him farewell and marched onwards, into the Territory of the Termites who guard the haunts of the terrible Cunmerrie.

The animals had told them that the Cunmerrie had been blinded by the fierce sun of this region, and that he struck only at night. Consequently they posted a sentry each night. Each day, as they marched through the plains of burning sand and the stones called gibbers, they asked any friendly animals or insects whether they had seen the Wobyang. But no one would admit to this, although they once met an old bandicoot who said he knew the Wobyang. On closer questioning it turned out that he had met him years ago and had not seen him since.

Then one night Arnica made a prediction which seemed to suggest that they could expect a dramatic development. During the march that day, each Hairy Peruvian had felt the presence of a strange force. It was nothing like the lure of the laughing kookaburra but far more ominous, and for the first time since the great storm in the Pacific that cracked the *Poppykettle* and drowned one of their friends they were very afraid.

Astute crept out into the darkness to keep watch, and the others huddled around the little fire to listen to Arnica as she acted out the dramatic preliminaries to her prediction. Then she chanted 'Forgotten I lost dreaming country I left forgotten lost.'

The Hairy Peruvians knew this introduction from other predictions, and they understood it to mean 'He who loses his dreaming also is lost.'

Arnica then continued 'The Wobyang is no more—just a warning gone before. Thus all who imitate the great will likewise meet a dreadful fate.'

She recited these lines quite boldly, paused, and then in a hoarse whisper concluded the prediction.

'Could we now not fate refute?

Watch out, Astute!'

As though this dramatic warning had been a cue, a terrible scream ripped through the silence of the night. The air was filled with a rushing as of a great wind, and out of the darkness above them a huge shadowy form swooped low over the fire.

It was the terrible Cunmerrie, appearing as though to give shape to their fears of the day. The beating of the great wings was like a whirlwind that scattered the burning coals of the fire, and the terrified Hairy Peruvians crouched like mice when a hawk flies overhead.

They heard a wavering cry of terror, and then the Cunmerrie was gone. For long moments they were paralysed by terror, but then Don Avante cried 'Astute! What has happened?'

The scattered coals of their fire had started a dozen small fires among the dry grass, and by this flickering light they ran to the place where Astute had been watching.

But he was gone without trace, and in the spot where he was when the talons of the Cunmerrie seized him there was only a huge feather.

Arnica's prediction had come so late that they were not prepared for this tragedy, and they stood in stunned silence as the scattered fires ran together into a great scrub fire that raged through the undergrowth. Suddenly the night was alive with birds, animals, and insects, startled by the fire and curious to know its cause. These creatures had been protected by the Cunmerrie, just as the creatures of the mountain had been protected by the Wobyang.

Without Astute to speak for them, the Hairy Peruvians were at a loss. Don Avante was fearless and always first into a fight, or first awake in the mornings, or first to finish his meals, but he could not match Astute and his shrewd powers of interrogation. The animals seemed to be very disturbed by the incident, and Don Avante found it even harder to talk to them because a big brolga seemed to be in charge and he was making a lot of fuss.

Suddenly, to Don Avante's surprise, quiet Arnago spoke up. She asked the brolga 'Does that beautiful feather actually belong to the Cunmerrie? It's strange that such a terrible creature should

Astute

have such lovely feathers, and we were told that he had skin like a reptile.'

The brolga was taken off-guard by such innocence and he answered quite politely. 'Ah, but the Cunmerrie has killed and eaten the Wobyang, and according to legend this means that a new creature will emerge. It will have parts of the spirits of both creatures, but a completely new form. We are told that it will have the colours and feathers of paradise.'

He cocked an eye at the beautiful feather and continued 'Obviously the transformation has begun, but the evil spirit of the Cunmerrie is still in possession. We are sorry that it has snatched away one of your group but we can't help you to get him back.'

A tiny animal, hidden behind the others, suddenly chirped 'But perhaps the Jacaranda Bellringers can help them,' but nobody answered.

Sadly, the Hairy Peruvians reconciled themselves to the loss of Astute. They spent some weeks talking with the animals in the Region of the Cunmerrie, and began to piece together the events leading up to the killing of the Wobyang. He had been very popular with all the animals, but those living within range of the Cunmerrie had thought it wiser not to admit their liking. Now that the Cunmerrie was changing they felt safe to talk, and the Hairy Peruvians gained some new and wonderful knowledge of the land.

They never went hungry now, and began to walk proudly when at last they wandered onwards. They had gathered such a stock of simple wisdom that their tiny forms seemed to grow in stature as well as confidence.

Often they thought they would move faster if they asked a big bird, or even a kangaroo, to give them a lift, but they were in no particular hurry and the easy independence of walking gave them a very close knowledge of the land.

But about a year after the disappearance of Astute, while they were still making their way back to the Wobyangs, they decided to make a side-trip over the desert to the western shoreline. They had heard about the Lobster Whistlers of the West, and Don Avante was very interested in these. In Peru, he and his fellow fishermen had used the technique of whistling anchovies into the nets cast from the reed boats of the Hairy Peruvians, and he was keen to study the system in this new land.

To make the long trip without too much effort he hired a goanna to carry them, and they set off to the west. Young Areca began to keep a diary on this trip, which took them 600 days. They might as

well have walked, but they were not to know that goannas are very sociable creatures. The one they hired kept on making detours to visit friends and relations along the way, and spending time on lengthy gossips about matters of no particular consequence. He was so unpredictable that Arnica gave up trying to make any predictions about the trip.

The goanna seemed very glad to get them off his back when they reached the windswept coast of the west, and they were equally glad to say good-bye to him. They gazed out over the Indian Ocean, which reminded them of the Pacific Ocean they had crossed with so much danger and difficulty, but they had no urge for another sea adventure.

Don Avante had been told to locate a fur seal as a guide, and when he found him he had to spend two or three days on 'smalltalk' of the kind which seals enjoy. It is not polite to ask sudden questions of seals, but Don Avante led slowly round to the subject of lobster whistling and the seal was quite forthcoming.

He said 'Personally, I gave up lobster whistling long ago, but I know quite a few who still practise the art. Most of them are squid and tired seagulls. They're too lazy to go out and catch the lobsters and so they simply whistle them into shallow water.'

He explained that mother lobsters lay their eggs in warm shallow waters, in the rock reefs close to shore. The eggs hatch into plankton, that drift out to sea for very long distances and then float back again, but of course a great many are eaten on the way. Those that survive develop into tiny lobsters with minds and personalities of their own, and consequently they begin to swim off in all directions.

However a good lobster whistler can attract their attention from the shore, and whistle them into the reef habitat where they can settle down and grow into adult lobsters. After this they are either eaten, or they reproduce to continue the cycle of life.

Arnago listened to this account and she became strangely affected. In her youth she had cared for juvenile anchovy along the coast of Peru, and she could now picture the great loss of life which must occur because nobody bothered to look after the tiny lobsters properly. She realised that if lobster whistling was made a matter of natural law, instead of something which occurred only when some lazy seals or squid happened to feel hungry, then hundreds of thousands of tiny lobsters would be guided safely back into the warm shallows. 'I must stay here and learn how to lobster-whistle,' she said firmly. 'It may have to be my life's work.'

26

Arnago

The others tried hard to persuade her not to desert them but she insisted on staying alone, to bring the message to creatures of the shoreline.

When the four remaining Hairy Peruvians returned to their base in the Wobyangs they had been away from it for twenty years. On their way back they called on Arrant, and found him in a terrible condition. He was quite thin and starved, but he still insisted on fighting the natural ways of animals and insects in the Unchosen Land instead of learning to understand their reasons. They mentioned the matter to a hairy-nosed wombat, who answered in the usual wombat way of approaching a matter from a different direction. He said, 'Since Dreamtime days I've followed my pad and those who would like to divert me are mad.'

This same wombat told them what had happened to the Feather of Paradise. They had hidden it in a tree just before they made their goanna trip to the west, but when they looked for it on their homeward journey it had disappeared. This made them very sad because it was their only souvenir of Astute and the only evidence of the fate of the Wobyang. They searched the whole area carefully without success, and when they met the wombat they asked him if he had seen it. He said 'Oldshadows come, feather go,' and they took this to mean that the mysterious Oldshadows had found the beautiful feather and carried it away.

The Hairy Peruvians settled into a quiet, almost domestic life in their green gully deep in the Wobyangs, and they often heard the animals talk about the Oldshadows. At last, almost 100 years after Arnica's arrival in the Unchosen Land, she began to make predictions about the Oldshadows, the first race of people in this huge country.

CHAPTER THREE

DURING THEIR LONG YEARS in the Wobyangs the Hairy Peruvians occupied themselves in various ways. Aloof gradually established large poppyseed plantations in the foothills and as far down as the coastal strip, so that they could always enjoy their traditional poppyseed cakes and poppyseed tea. When they opened the last bags of poppyseed that had arrived in the *Poppykettle* they found a number of peppercorns mixed with the seed, and Areca introduced this new plant into the Unchosen Land. With the help of Aloof she grew seedlings, harvested the crop, and then grew more seedlings until she had small plantations. Arnica encouraged this project, to meet a purpose many years in the future.

Hairy Peruvians, like other imaginary races, live to be at least 300 years old unless they are accidentally killed. Some live to be 450 or more. Don Avante was nearly 200 when he sailed in the *Poppykettle*, but Arnica was much younger and Areca was only three. Areca was now older than a human grandmother, and she like all the others was becoming tired of their monotonous life in the lonely Wobyangs.

There was not much to do apart from tending the plantations and talking to the birds and animals. As the years went by they learned how to do this very well and gained a great deal of information, but animal conversation can become very boring because they gossip a great deal about all the members of their huge families and they are very wary of talking about things they are afraid of or do not understand. For example it was hard to persuade them to talk about the Oldshadows, and even harder to glean anything definite about the mysterious Jacaranda Bellringers.

The Hairy Peruvians had not seen anything of the Oldshadows during their wanderings over the Unchosen Land, but from their high lookouts on the Wobyangs they sometimes saw the smoke from little fires arising out of the distant plains. They began to wonder more and more about such matters, and they also felt very curious about the fate of old Arrant and his strange farming experiment. At the same time, Arnica began to make new predictions about strange people and dangerous adventures, and if these were to come true they would have to leave the safety of their home.

It was not easy to make the decision to move away, and to leave the plantations they had established. They knew that the animals would not look after these, and so they decided to carry the best of the seedlings with them for Arrant to plant on his farm. He could maintain the crops while they searched for the Oldshadows.

The four travellers arrived at Arrant's farm during harvest, and they were quite impressed with the wide range of strange plants that he had managed to keep alive during a series of dry years. He had a great deal to tell them about his battle to survive. At one time, the two great rivers which met near his farm had flooded over and washed away everything he had planted. At another time they had dried up altogether. Often his seeds did not grow at all, frequently they were carried away by ants, and even when the young sprouts poked through the earth a family of hungry kangaroos or a flock of cockatoos would nibble them away.

Don Avante asked him why he continued to struggle so hard. 'You are a fisherman, not a farmer,' he said, but Arrant answered only 'This is a matter between me and the land.'

His crops included some plants which had come with them from Peru. While they were sailing aboard the *Poppykettle* they had always saved up the odds and ends of seeds and other rubbish which they found in the sacks of poppyseed, and they had given these to Arrant to start his new farm. They included a few 'greasy pods' which nobody had seen before, and a small collection of burrs from a weed which had smothered the Andes. Don Avante had collected these burrs together and he carried them in a small bag which he kept sealed, fearing that if they escaped they would spread as they had done in Peru.

The Hairy Peruvians could now see the result of the seeds they had given to Arrant. After more than 100 annual harvests his farm had produced a range of new plants. Some were useful as food and others as medicines, but a few had spread out of control and were useless. After a slow start the 'greasy pods' had germinated and grown into healthy jojoba beans.

The four wanderers gave their poppyseed and peppercorn seedlings to Arrant and saw them safely planted, and then were free to wander again. Don Avante, Arnica, Areca, and Aloof bade farewell to Arrant and renewed their search for the Oldshadows who had taken the Feather of Paradise.

They did not understand that the Oldshadows were human, like the Noble Inca of their own country, and that those who had taken the feather would have died long ago. But now that they were looking seriously for the Oldshadows they began to find many signs, especially along the river. Where the river deepened and formed a pond they found giant footsteps in the mud, and reeds had been broken. Now and again they skirted the ashes of a campfire which had blackened the earth and stones for some way around. Stark white bones of fish and animals were scattered in the ashes.

A flock of galahs feeding in the red gums gave them their first warning that the Oldshadows were not far away. Their scouts had seen them fishing from bark canoes some way downstream, below a fish trap built in the river.

Don Avante, the old fisherman, pricked up his ears at the mention of a fish trap, and he urged the others to stop gossiping with the talkative galahs and hurry on.

To a fisherman, a fish trap made of stones and plaited reeds is a wonderful contrivance. But to a trapped cod fish in a hurry it can be most annoying. When they reached the trap they found it contained a big fat cod, and the language which he used to describe the Oldshadows suggested that these people were not as gentle and harmless as the galahs had indicated. The Hairy Peruvians accepted this warning in the same way that they accepted that codfish are bad-tempered and uncouth, and nearly always overweight.

They had just finished their conversation with the codfish when they heard low voices and the ripple of water, and looked up to see two bark canoes glide around the bend in the river below the trap. A tall lean Oldshadow stood upright in each canoe, using his long spear to propel the simple craft. A small cooking fire smouldered on stones in the bottom of each canoe, and the smoke from these partly obscured other Oldshadows sitting in the canoes.

The Oldshadows were even blacker than the Armies of the Urubamba, who used to fight the Noble Inca in the days before the Shining Spaniards conquered Peru. They wore no clothes and their bodies were smooth and sleek. Arnica quickly calculated that between twelve and eighteen Hairy Peruvians would have to stand on one another's shoulders to reach the hair of the Oldshadow standing in the leading canoe.

Before the Oldshadows appeared, the river had been a scene of busy occupation. A water rat was munching a yabbie he had caught for his breakfast, the galahs were feeding in the trees, and a family of beautiful white egrets were fishing in the shallows. But

31

now every creature gave his or her alarm cry of '*Humans*!' and fled or flew away as fast as possible. (Except for the cod, who continued grumbling and swearing in the trap). Never since the days of the Cunmerrie had the Hairy Peruvians seen such a startling commotion.

They had no special fear of humans, and the three old travellers remembered the human islanders who helped them when the *Poppykettle* was in danger of being dashed onto a Pacific coral reef. But Areca could not remember anything about humans, and as the canoes of the Oldshadows glided closer she and the others looked to Don Avante for guidance. He was a recognised authority in the way that imaginary creatures should deal with human beings.

Everyone understood that humans, of every race and colour, believed themselves to be superior to all other animals. They considered matters differently, and spoke of themselves as though they were at the centre of everything with everything revolving around them.

The lore of imaginary creatures directs that they must never talk directly to a human being except in very unusual situations, and that they must seek some other means of communication. The great problem of course, is that very few humans will admit to having seen such small people as Hairy Peruvians, and they do not feel safe about talking to them. If they do happen to see them then they are likely to say 'I must have imagined it.' Of course this is quite right, but humans are most unwilling to admit that the things they imagine can very often be more real than those which they can touch and handle.

The Hairy Peruvians considered that this strange attitude was a good example of those things which make humans much more complex than other animals.

Don Avante prepared himself for the encounter and felt a sideways approach developing. Remembering similar situations, he thought it was always difficult to be sure you had the right approach to ensure a positive reaction from a human. They are always so unpredictable.

But he did not have time to say anything as the Oldshadows came closer and closer, until they were towering above the Hairy Peruvians. First one, then another, then all the Oldshadows spotted the tiny figures. They looked away disbelievingly, not wanting to say anything in case the others laughed at them, and then looked again to make sure that their eyes did not deceive them.

But one very old Oldshadow, who was tending the fire in the bottom of a canoe, reacted without delay. As soon as he saw the Hairy Peruvians he exclaimed 'The children of the Wobyang!'

The others turned to him, as though seeking his protection from enchantment by unwelcome spirits. With eyes fixed on the four tiny figures, he said 'Long ago, the Munkumboli spoke of a new force, outside the Dreamtime. A force exerted by spirits in human form, who can speak all tongues of humans and animals and lived with the last Wobyang. The Bellringers told the Munkumboli that these new spirits, never before seen by we Oldshadows, will walk the land forever. These must be those spirits—the children of the Wobyang!'

When Don Avante heard these words he forgot his plan for a sideways approach. He realised that the Oldshadows must be different from all other human beings. It was obvious that, unlike so many humans, they understood that what is imaginary may be real and that what seems real may sometimes be imaginary.

He was about to speak when Arnica interrupted. She was quick to sense an exciting new prediction and when the Oldshadow said '. . . will walk the land forever' she rather aggressively challenged his authority for the statement. She sounded almost offended that someone else should predict the future.

But Don Avante, in a quieter voice, asked 'Did you speak of the Bellringers? Can you tell us where to find them?'

The Oldshadow was understandably confused. He had never encountered such happenings before, especially when he was enjoying a quiet day's fishing on the river. He looked from one to another of the tiny folk, and then answered Don Avante. 'I have never seen the Bellringers, whom those of northern parts know as the Jacaranda Bellringers. The Munkumboli, our wise leaders and guardians of the gates to the Dreamtime, are the only ones who can see and hear them.'

He paused for a long time and everything was silent: a strange silence broken almost rudely by the lapping of the waters over the stones of the trap. Even the codfish had fallen silent.

Then the Oldshadow spoke again, with deep reverence. 'The Bellringers do not live on the land as we do, and they do not have a shape such as you people, the Children of Wobyang. They can be found only within your mind.'

He paused again, seeming to consult some unseen authority, and then continued 'I am one of those who can show you how to find them, but we must go together to the place of the Munkumboli.'

The Hairy Peruvians felt great excitement. By chance, they had stumbled upon aspects of the Unchosen Land that reached beyond mere survival. After decades of proud walking, they seemed close to discovering the symbols which might unlock the heart of the vast land.

The Hairy Peruvians could not have kept up with the tireless pacing of the ancient Oldshadow, as he walked through the great stretches of bushland between the river and the place of the Munkumboli. He carried them in the palm of his old gnarled hand, and as he walked for many weeks they talked to him about various mysteries.

They encountered many Oldshadow families, and when at last they reached the Munkumboli they found their leader living in a wurley with many others camped nearby. They thought he looked very much like the Oldshadow who had carried them so far, and they thought that he must be human after all. This was rather disappointing, because all humans look so much alike that it is difficult to distinguish those who are important from those who are not so important, especially when they are naked like the Oldshadows.

The chief Munkumbli received them kindly and said he would lead them to the Jacaranda Bellringers, but warned them not to ask questions of anyone along the way. They expected to set off on another great journey, but he simply told them to listen quietly and began this chant:—

> *Jacaranda hacaroo*
> *Jacaranda hacaroo*
> *Ips witch graduation bells*
> *Chiming for the lonely from Peru*
> *Tolling for . . .*

His chant continued, and as it went on a vivid image formed in the minds of the listeners. They saw, as though in a dream, the Bellringers crowded around a great cauldron in a forest of colour. One after another they struck the cauldron with axes, some hitting more than once and others missing a turn as though they had been orchestrated. The tune they tolled was their message, and it became as clear as though they had spoken.

The wise Bellringers knew that now the Hairy Peruvians had met the Oldshadows, the Realtime was about to meet the Dreamtime. The time had come for a choice to be made between the

37

two, and for a decision as to belief in predictions of the future. The Munkumboli had always made predictions which governed the Oldshadows way of life, and they had relied upon information received from the spirits of the Dreamtime. The Hairy Peruvians always made predictions from information received in the Realtime.

The Bellringers said, through the tolling rhythm of their tune, that Dreamtime and Realtime must now compete, to decide which of their predictions was the most reliable.

The wise Bellringers also knew that such a contest would appeal to both the Hairy Peruvians and the Munkumboli. It would have to continue for a long time, and many predictions would be cast before the determining forecast was uttered. The side that made the correct prediction on the outcome of the contest would be the authority for the future, at least until another source emerged to claim leadership.

The dream faded and the vision of the Bellringers was gone, but the message remained. Just before the vision disappeared, Areca was about to ask what had happened to the Feather of Paradise. But she was too late and her opportunity had gone.

The Munkumboli leader told them that such a contest had never been held before, and so it must be held at the place called The Black Stump. This was chosen because it is the place where truth and fantasy are separated, and also because no two people can ever agree on its location. The Munkumboli, however, knew the exact position of the Black Stump. It stands precisely where north, south, east, and west all meet together.

'This being the case, it will take a long time for all the Munkumboli to gather,' he remarked. 'Therefore there is no hurry for us to reach the Black Stump.'

But as they progressed towards it they met Munkumboli delegates assembling from all regions of the great Unchosen Land. Each group wore different decorations to indicate where they belonged. Their black bodies were painted with white, brown, and ochre taken from the earth, and brilliant feathers were fastened in bands around their arms and legs. The groups greeted each other quietly and with great respect.

The Hairy Peruvians watched their arrival with great interest, not only in the way that rival assesses rival before combat but also because they felt the great importance of the event. Never had such a happening occurred in their homeland. Here, in their Unchosen Land, they were to pit the skills which seemed natural to them against the best that could be mustered from the whole race of Oldshadows.

Areca studied each new arrival even more closely than did her companions, because she felt sure that one of them would be wearing the Feather of Paradise. Arnica had actually predicted that it would appear at the contest, but nobody had taken much notice. But she had been right. An old Munkumboli from the southern riverlands made a grand entry just before the challenge was to begin, and Areca saw the lost feather from the Cunmerrie protruding from an ornate woven headband and reaching high above his head. Obviously he was much respected because everyone stood up as he entered the arena around the fire.

When they had settled down again this Munkumboli was the first to speak. He looked across the fire at the Hairy Peruvians and said 'We see the world around us through the screen of everything that we believe to be true. Sometimes, that which we believe to be true makes it very difficult to see the real truth.'

He paused for a long time, and then continued 'Which is the most real, a man or his spirit? A man dies, but does his spirit die also? Surely it would be a great waste if we were given so many powers, to know the beauty of the world, the joy of love, the pleasures of our skills and our strength, if they were only to vanish in the twinkling of an eye?'

All the meeting murmured agreement, and the old Munkumboli said 'We believe that a man and a spirit are two separate things, and that his spirit may wander freely when he sleeps and leave him forever when he dies. Our spirits travel in the Dreamtime, and in the Dreamtime country they have experiences and adventures similar to ours when we are awake.'

He gazed around at all those who listened in silence. 'We belong to the land and the land belongs to us. Without it, we cannot survive. And without us, and all the other creatures who live upon this earth, the land would have no meaning. Therefore we believe that our spirits may enter into all the other creatures and features of the land, and that theirs may enter into us. A rock or a tree, a clump of spinifex grass or the ripple of water on a stream, may possess the spirit of an Oldshadow whose body vanished long ago. The life of this world continues forever and we are but part of its endless procession.'

The old Munkumboli spoke for a long time on such matters, before he fell silent and gestured to Don Avante to speak. The leader of the Hairy Peruvians stood up and addressed the great

gathering whose black skins gleamed in the firelight, which flickered upon their body paintings and upon the brilliant feathers of their decorations.

He said 'Our way is different from yours but I do not know how to explain it. We understand it ourselves but I fear that others may not understand us, and they will never understand until they believe that imagination is as important as reality.'

After this statement he introduced Arnica, who would represent the Hairy Peruvians in the future-telling contest. Areca acted as her assistant and kept notes of everything that was said.

The contest began and continued almost non-stop for many days and nights. Each Munkumboli made a speech followed by a prediction, and Arnica equalled this with one of her predictions. At the end of the contest they all faced the problem of assessing the reliability of the predictions, because no one could yet tell whether any of them would come true.

The Oldshadows' predictions certainly were more colourful than those of the Hairy Peruvians, because the Dreamtime generates more imaginative images than the Realtime. But this fact was not enough to win the contest, and at last they all decided to choose ten predictions and submit them to the Jacaranda Bellringers for a decision.

Each member of the gathering opened his mind to the Bellringers while Areca read out the ten predictions, and the reaction was quite definite. Only the first half of the prediction was spoken aloud, because the second half was so strange that it could be heard only in the minds of the listeners. The first half ran: —

Six Peruvians proudly walk our land
Five found symbols never seen before
Now four mark us with new gospels
Soon three the rivals will be
And two greet a Lilywhite fleet
Burdened with values and seeking strange ends
Then one is alone whom Areca shall be

Arnica had been very impressed by this prediction but she believed it should not have been accepted from a Munkumboli because it seemed to draw upon Realtime rather than Dreamtime imaginings. But one must not query a prediction and she accepted the decision with good grace.

During the contest she had been greatly impressed by the

Dreamtime imagery. Now that the ultimate authority had ruled in favour of the Munkumboli she came to a sudden but firm decision. She would seek the aid of the Munkumboli to enter the Dreamtime forever, so that she might study and preserve the myths and spirits which had become vividly real to her during the days of prediction.

Her three companions were horrified. 'If you leave us, how shall we obtain the predictions which shape our lives?' they argued.

She answered 'Areca is old enough now. It is time she took up my role.'

At last, with deep sighs, they agreed to her decision, but shrewd Don Avante used this opportunity for some bargaining. When he saw that the Munkumboli were eager to accept Arnica and pass her through into the Dreamtime, he said they must give him the Feather of Paradise in exchange. Reluctantly they agreed, and the three Hairy Peruvians bade farewell to Arnica as she was escorted into the glowing mists of the Dreamtime. They knew they would not see her again, but they would feel her influence through the Oldshadows of the future.

The contest had been a great success because the Munkumboli now respected the powers of the Hairy Peruvians, and in future would consult them on matters of the Realtime. The Hairy Peruvians had equal respect for these humans whose spirits sometimes inhabited their bodies and sometimes emerged through a myriad different forms.

The two groups left the Black Stump and then parted to go their different ways: The Hairy Peruvians, with the Feather of Paradise, to walk the shadow line between reality and fantasy; the Munkumboli to resume the spirit path of their tribal wanderings.

Arrant

CHAPTER FOUR

IN REALTIME CALCULATIONS, THE date of the prediction challenge probably was about 1700. After that time it is hard to trace the story of the Hairy Peruvians for something like fifty years, and one must rely upon half-heard legends passed down through generations of Oldshadows.

It seems possible that Arnago died during this period, and it is believed that she witnessed a distressing episode when Dutch Lilywhite sailors were wrecked upon her lobster reefs of the west coast. But there is no certainty of this, and for all we know she may still live along the seashores of the Unchosen Land. The evidence against this includes the fact that the lobster population of that region has declined considerably. This may well be for lack of an experienced lobster whistler, to guide the small fry into the safety of the reefs.

Lonely Arrant died in 1751, but he did not die alone. Areca, whose powers of prediction strengthened as she grew older, uttered a prediction which foretold his death, and she together with Don Avante and Aloof hurried to Arrant's farm at the junction of the two rivers. He died soon after they arrived, and his last wish was that they should maintain his precious plant farm experiments.

Some of the products of his farming had become hardy plants which spread themselves over great distances. They had produced many variations and some were prolific with seeds and beautiful flowers. It is not possible to describe all of them because many of the original names have been forgotten, and replaced by other names which the Oldshadows and then the Lilywhites gave to this flora of the deserts and plains.

After the death of Arrant the three survivors considered how they might carry out his final desire. It caused a great deal of argument because Areca and the two elders had fallen into this bad habit. During the years of wandering they had become rivals rather than colleagues. Sometimes two of them would join forces against a third, but usually each would stand firm on a personal point of view. It was a sad state of affairs, because they argued so resolutely that, on occasion, they would stay in one place for a year because they could not agree on which direction to go.

But at least they agreed that they did not want to settle down as farmers, and the problem of obeying Arrant's dying wish kept them talking for a very long time. They tried to interest Arrant's wombat and bandicoot labourers in taking over the farm, but they soon realised that this would not work. The wombats and bandicoots had worked well under Arrant's friendly control, but they had soon reverted to plundering the harvest and digging their holes amongst it.

However a wombat plot manager, named Burrawong, cast out a suggestion which·was as vague as most ideas which occur to wombats, and they seized gratefully upon this and established a plan around it. They called it the Big Burrawong Scheme.

Each of them agreed to select one species of plant which had done well during the two centuries of trials. They would carry the seeds on their wanderings, and plant one seed each evening just before Areca made her usual prediction for the next day. They knew that at least some of the seeds would germinate, and spread useful plants throughout the Unchosen Land.

To help their choice they consulted with the Oldshadows, and Areca made a series of long-range predictions. The Oldshadows suggested that since peppercorn trees provided a flavouring for an otherwise dull diet of kangaroo, witchetty grub, and snake, they would be glad to see peppercorns planted at every few hours journey throughout the land. Areca undertook to do this as her part of abiding by the will of Arrant.

Aloof was less imaginative. He chose to plant poppyseeds to feed future generations of Hairy Peruvians, and completely ignored Areca's prediction that no more of their community would arrive in the Unchosen Land. It was most discourteous and very unusual to ignore a prediction, but he and Areca had just had an extremely bitter argument.

Don Avante had listened very carefully to Areca's furthest ranging predictions. More and more of them concerned the Lilywhites, and he slowly became convinced that she was not simply· influenced by the Munkumboli prediction mentioning these people. Some of her predictions about the Lilywhites were hardly credible, because it seemed impossible to him that any people could be so cruel, ingenious, foolish, and imaginative all at the same time.

But he decided to rely upon her, and his mind was made up by her prediction that 'In far off times, Lilywhites will come to understand that freakish art must not be mistaken for creativity. In

48

those days the oil of the greasy bean will warm the toes of the Lilywhite and turn the wheels of his world.'

Don Avante tried hard to understand the meaning of this prediction, but it meant nothing to him except that it mentioned the greasy bean. This decided him to carry seeds of the greasy bean for planting on his wanderings. He knew that they grew well in marshy places, and the beans provided good medicine for the complaints he had begun to suffer in his old age.

For the next few decades they wandered the Unchosen Land, planting their seeds as they went. They renewed old acquaintances among the birds and animals and met the children and grandchildren of old animal friends. Often they stayed at the camps of the Oldshadows, but they heard nothing from Arnica until one night in 1770.

Areca had barely finished her prediction for the day when a Munkumboli who lived in the tribal area paced into the camp. He had been sent with a message from the Dreamtime, and he asked them to join him in chanting a contact with the Bellringers. The Bellringers would then connect them with Arnica.

When Arnica at last spoke to them she seemed vague and far away. She wanted them to investigate a Realtime phenomenon which she suspected had become confused with some powerful Dreamtime spirits. She could not leave her world and return to the Realtime, and so they must act as her delegates.

She told them how to find a place on the east coast, and told them that one day it would be known as Eden. They must go to its tidal reef gardens, and observe the Dance of the Periwinkles. She said that some spirits in the Dreamtime believed the dance ritual of certain periwinkles contained deep and powerful future-telling, and so they must observe the nature of the dance very carefully and be attentive for any messages which it conveyed.

Don Avante and Areca eagerly undertook the project because it was a relief from their eternal wandering and planting. Aloof did not much care for a new adventure but he tagged along with them, grumbling most of the time.

At Eden, they searched the reefs for the Periwinkles. Areca had foreseen that the dancing would be performed only at a flood tide, in a prediction stating:—

> *While the sun and the rain live, these shall be*
> *Till a last wind's breath upon all these blowing*
> *Rolls the sea*

50

She called the seashore 'The Marginal World,' and said 'The shore has a double nature, changing with the swing of the tides, belonging now to the land and now to the sea.'

They were peering into a rock pool garden as she spoke, watching the shells and pebbles whirl around as each wavelet surged around them.

She continued 'On the ebb tide, the Marginal World knows the harsh extremes of the land world. It is exposed to heat and cold, to wind, and to drying sun. On the flood tide it is a water world, returning to the quiet calm and stability of the open sea. Only the most hardy can survive in such a realm, to dance forever between the tides.'

Then they knew that they had been watching the dance although they had been seeking something more specific. The simple shells abandoned by departed spirits, and moving perpetually to and fro under the impulse of the tides until they are ground into sand, indeed have a great meaning in their dance. But it would take a lifetime of careful watching to interpret its meaning.

The three wanderers stayed among the reefs of the Marginal World for a very long time. They gathered the wisdom of the region as a wandering shearwater gathers food among the rocks and weed and carries it to her nestlings. They carried their information to the dry land above the high tide mark, to digest what they had found.

During this time, Don Avante made friends with a moonbird who had just flown in from the Land of the Long White Cloud. Don Avante had heard of this place, although he had never been there. Many years before, as they voyaged across the Pacific in the *Poppykettle*, they had passed the long canoes of sea-travellers migrating from the land to islands of the central Pacific.

The moonbird was shy at first but soon became quite talkative. He talked about his recent long flight and how tired it had made him. 'I felt I could no longer endure the endless beating of my wings, but then I saw a strange island beneath me. Moonbird legends do not tell of any islands in that place, but I was happy to fly down and rest upon it. Never have I seen such an island before. Three great trees grew upon it, but instead of leaves they had great white wings. The ground was flat, and made of timber, and human creatures walked upon it, and it seemed to me that the island moved through the water. But how can that be?'

Don Avante remembered a prediction made by Areca, and he

questioned the moonbird more closely. At last he realised that the moonbird had alighted on one of the great white windships, such as those used by the Shining Spaniards when they conquered Peru.

Don Avante was both excited and disturbed. He discussed the matter with the others, and they concluded that the age of the Lilywhites was about to begin in the Unchosen Land. On the one hand they feared the worst, believing that these Lilywhites might be similar to the Shining Spaniards with all their greed and cruelty. On the other hand they knew that a prediction cannot be changed and that they must not attempt to pervert it.

Eventually they reached a decision, and its outcome can only be described in the words of an old seafarer who lived out his last days in the Lilywhite settlement at Sydney Cove. He was known to be a great spinner of yarns but he claimed to have been to so many places that few people believed all his stories, especially when he had drunk a good deal of rum.

He said 'When I were sailing with young Lieutenant Jimmy Cook, seeking the place what they called New Holland, no one could never understand how he found his way so handy. Some there was who said he must have had maps made by the Portuguese, or the likes o' them, especially when he steered the *Endeavour* in among them reefs along the northern coastline.

'But young Jimmy never had no maps that I heard of. He drew his own maps as he went along, see? Or charts, as you'd call them in a proper seafaring way. I seen them with my own eyes, laying 'em out on his cabin table and him scratching away on them with a ruler and a quill pen.

'One day I were sent down to his cabin with some message or other, and there he was scratching his head and staring down at his charts. When I come in he looks at me sharp-like, and asks "Have you been playing around with these thunderation charts of mine?"'

'"What me, sir?" I says. "I can't read nor write, so it couldn't be me."'

'"That's passing strange," he said. "Here's someone been drawing in the coastline we haven't even come to yet, and marking in all kinds of rocks and reefs and hidden dangers."'

The old sailor's story gives some clue to Don Avante's suggestion. Probably he and the others persuaded one of the larger seabirds, possibly an albatross, to carry them out to the *Endeavour*. Once aboard, they would have used Don Avante's knowledge of seamanship, and Areca's powers of prediction, to

54

help James Cook's explorations. In this way they would have acted in the true spirit of the Third People.

A study of the Journals of James Cook, for the period Tuesday 12 June to Monday 18 June 1770, will discover a series of curious references and decisions that suggest intervention by a source that knows what the future holds. It may well be that this enabled him to steer his crippled craft through apparently unknown waters and hazards into a safe harbour, when the usual Lilywhite action would have been to retrace his progress through waters already charted.

After this incident the three travellers resumed their wandering, through a long period of discontent. They became preoccupied with thought of the Lilywhites and gave many warnings to the friends they had made in the Unchosen Land but to little or no effect. The Oldshadows could not understand them and the birds and animals were too busy with their usual occupations.

The three travellers continued to plant their seeds and to check on those already planted, with varying success. Most of the peppercorns developed into strong trees wherever they were planted and some of them still survive today. Don Avante's greasy jojoba beans survived only near water, and Aloof's poppies grew well into juvenile plants but then vanished entirely. They did not simply shrivel up and die like some water-starved plant, they just disappeared.

Don Avante suspected that the terrible plague locusts had eaten the poppies, just as they ate everything else in their path, but he did not want to frighten the others with these thoughts. They had always dreaded an attack by locust armies on the march. But Aloof insisted that they should seek out the destroyer of his poppy plantings, and this mission led them into the swamps and billabong regions just north of the location of Arrant's farm.

One hot summer afternoon they saw the locusts. Battalions of them surrounded the lush grass and poppies of the old farm area, and the three tiny people crouched low behind a stone to watch the appalling destruction. Platoon after company of the locusts fell upon the plants and munched through them with their terrible jaws, and the Hairy Peruvians were so mesmerised by the scene that they let themselves be surrounded by the hordes. With sudden horror they realised they were trapped.

Don Avante quickly calculated their chances of keeping the locusts at bay, until they found an escape route over the soft mudflats between the pools of the billabong. He knew that any

attempt held frightful dangers, but any risk was better than certain death in the jaws of a locust.

The time had come for his weapon of last resort. For more than 200 years the pouch at his belt had carried the burrs, brought from Peru in the sacks of poppyseed, that he feared would spread a fearful weed throughout the land.

When a dozen locusts hurried greedily towards the fugitives, he opened the pouch and took out one burr seed. He threw it towards the leading locust, who pounced upon it and tried to swallow it in one gulp. The spines of the burr choked him, and as he writhed in pain the other locusts set upon him and tore him apart.

Areca was horrified by this scene of ruthless cannibalism, which was repeated again and again as Don Avante acted as their rearguard, casting one seed after another in the path of the locusts.

At last they reached the edge of the billabong, and safety lay across the mud to the place where two pelicans were feeding. Don Avante gasped 'Quickly—hurry to them and ask them to help us! I'll try to keep the locusts away!'

Stepping backwards all the time he threw the last few burrs at the terrible insects, and then turned to run after the others. He slid on the mud, fell into a pool of muddy water, and never even saw the great yabby which grabbed him with its spiny claws.

From the back of one of the white pelicans, Areca and Aloof looked down to see the grey-green slime close over the palm of the old hand. Outstretched fingers clutched at the air and then disappeared.

Don Avante was gone, dragged down into the waters of the Burrawong Billabong. The terrible summer dragged on, the locusts spread their destruction, and the awful burrs were loose in the land because the locusts, in their greed, had not paused to snap up all of them.

CHAPTER FIVE

THE LOSS OF DON AVANTE was only the beginning of dramatic events which were to change the Unchosen Land forever. The awful experience made Areca and Aloof flee from the inland towards the coast, and after long journeying they arrived at the shores of a great harbour just in time to watch the arrival of the Lilywhites.

Areca and Aloof spoke little together by that time, but as they rested in the grasses by the shore Aloof said 'Your most dramatic predictions should now come true.'

Areca nodded, and said nothing. As the days and weeks passed, and then the months and years, the two remaining Hairy Peruvians occupied their time in watching the strange behaviour of the Lilywhites. They seemed content to pitch their tents anywhere, instead of looking for the right signs as the Hairy Peruvians had learned to do, and they also broke up the land with such enthusiasm and energy that Areca thought it must be some ritual like her daily future-telling.

As the Lilywhites settled themselves into the Unchosen Land, Areca and Aloof became conscious that they had brought members of the Third People with them. They were not like any of the Third People whom the Hairy Peruvians had known before, but it was obvious that they had developed out of the imagination of the Lilywhites. Areca and Aloof did not speak to them to begin with but only observed them closely, until they ran into a little group picking their way along a path through the grass. They eyed each other without hostility, for the Third People are too wise to fight, and soon opened a conversation.

Areca learned that the lilywhites gave the name of 'gnomes' to these little people who had come with them, and that larger communities lived in the storyland of Lilywhite minds all over the world. When these gnomes heard Areca refer to them as the Third People, they asked her why. She answered 'The Oldshadows are the First People, the Lilywhites are the Second People, and so we folk must call ourselves the Third People.'

This was a good enough reason, and the newcomers soon became very friendly. Some of them helped to build a home for Areca and Aloof, at a place which the Lilywhites called Lavender Bay, while others chose to live more closely to the Lilywhites on whom they had become dependent.

Aloof had grown sullen and withdrawn, and he seemed determined to revenge the centuries he had wandered the Unchosen Land. He chose the Lilywhites for his revenge because of their ill-treatment of his friends the Oldshadows, and gathered together a band of brave helpers from among the Third People. He named his gang the Kirribilli Boys.

They had noted that there were two kinds of Lilywhites, and to these they gave the names of the *Uppers* and the *Lowers*. The two types were easy to distinguish. The Uppers wore gold chains and bright clothing, while the Lowers wore iron chains and ragged clothing.

Of course the Kirribilli Boys could not mount a direct attack upon the Uppers, and so Aloof devised a curious technique which he called 'The Strategy for Symbolic Retribution.' A good example of this technique was the Affair of the Calico Cat.

The Calico Cat belonged to the Reverend Samuel Marsden, a leader among the Uppers. Areca sensed that Marsden believed in some peculiar combination of the Realtime and the Dreamtime, and sometimes she heard him speak of these matters to gatherings of the Lowers. But since his talks usually preceded some moment of horrifying cruelty, she could not take him seriously. Sometimes she heard the Lowers call him 'The Flogging Parson.'

He was just the kind of Lilywhite to attract Aloof's desire for revenge, even though it had to be indirect revenge carried out in the sideways manner with which Third People must deal with humans.

Aloof and the Kirribilli Boys spied carefully upon the Marsden family, and discovered that their most cherished possession was Calico Cat. This pampered feline had been imported from Paris and was the pride of the Marsden household. Like most Calico Cats she had a violent nature and frequently threw tantrums when she did not get her own way, and this made Aloof's revenge harder to carry out.

But he trained his greencoated Kirribilli Boys in Calico Cat identification, tracking, capture, and mild torture. When they heard that Marsden had cruelly punished one of the Lowers, the cat commandos moved with speed and precision. They caught Calico Cat, tied her down, and teased her until Aloof was ready to extract symbolic retribution by swiftly and dramatically extracting one or more of her long whiskers.

Aloof

Of course Aloof and the cat commandos could have told Calico Cat exactly why they were treating her in this way but they preferred to let her work it out for herself. Slowly the bewildered animal understood that unless her master changed his habits she would never be free from raids by the annoying 'Green Boys,' as they sometimes called themselves. She did what she could to discourage her master from continuing his harsh punishments but naturally he did not understand her deferential purring and urgent cat-calling and took them simply as a tribute to himself. Finally she could stand no more of the ritual de-whiskering and ran away from home to live in the Blue Mountains, while Marsden was away on holiday in New Zealand.

Areca was aware of Aloof's activities but she chose not to interfere with them because she knew that he was due to die on New Year's Day 1810. She contented herself with the elliptical comment 'Revenge may be neat, but 'tis never sweet. The harm once begun is rarely undone.'

Now that Areca was alone she found herself becoming more and more involved in the affairs of the Lilywhites, and this brought her a severe reprimand when she contacted Arnica through the Jacaranda Bellringers. Arnica said that Lilywhite treatment of the Oldshadows was enabling Realtime to intrude into Dreamtime and causing great distress and confusion to the Mumkumboli. She accused Areca of flouting the lore by interfering in Lilywhite affairs directly instead of taking the traditional sideways approach, but Areca found it was impossible to save herself from falling into the devious and materialistic ways of the Lilywhites.

She tried to avoid this by devoting herself to the newly arrived Third People, and teaching them the lessons she had learned about living in the Unchosen Land. Most of the new immigrants were either ignorant or had gathered the tattered remnants of a Lilywhite approach to life, and they could not grasp her instructions on how to grasp from nature the vital signs that are essential for foretelling the future.

She set some Third People to work alongside some struggling Lilywhite settlements along the great inland rivers that she knew so well. These Third People developed into the Reach People, who shared habitats among the river gums with the more adventurous and ambitious Lilywhite pioneers. Areca hoped that the Reach People would be able to help the Lilywhites with the problems of settlement.

A migrating moonbird interrupted Areca's activities with a

strange story. It was that of the jewel boxes which had lost their keys.

These three boxes, of priceless workmanship, had lain for centuries in the cathedral at Lima in Peru. They were known to contain great wealth in jewels, stolen from the Noble Inca, but the keys had vanished long ago. Each box had two locks, and many skilful locksmiths had attempted to open them without success. The Shining Spaniards were unwilling to break them open because this would spoil the boxes themselves.

A notorious pirate, Benito Benita, knew about the boxes and had for a long time plotted to steal them. But he was in the same quandary as the Shining Spaniards. He could not open the boxes without the keys, and if he broke open the boxes he would lose a great deal of the value of his loot.

Suddenly he remembered the legend which passed up and down the seacoast of Peru: about the Hairy Peruvians who had stolen brass keys to ballast their tiny craft *Poppykettle*.

As a seafarer, he guessed that they had sailed to the west and ended in the Unchosen Land, which had now been settled by the Lilywhites and was known to him although he had not been there.

The moonbird said that Benito Benita had put all his guesses together, raided the cathedral and stolen the boxes, and set sail for the Unchosen Land. He would arrive very soon, and the moonbird said he was heading for the spot where the Hairy Peruvians had abandoned the *Poppykettle* on the seashore.

Areca made up her mind immediately. She was unable to make any predictions about Benito Benita's search for the keys, and so she felt compelled to do whatever she could to frustrate him.

For the first time in nearly two centuries she travelled back to the Wobyangs and then towards the seashore. It was a long hard journey, and she sometimes asked local animals and birds to help her cross the rivers and hills of the south-eastern coastline.

Everything in the Wobyangs looked very familiar but none of the descendants of the Wobyang Refugees was interested in her stories of the old days except for two big black crows. They took pity on the lonely little woman and listened to her story, and became so interested that they walked with her over the carpet of soft needles beneath the she-oaks until they reached the seashore.

And there, close to the place which the Lilywhites had named Limeburners Point, not very far from the Lilywhite settlement known to Oldshadows as Geelong, was a pirate galleon riding at anchor. They crept to the shelter of the grey trees overlooking

Limeburners Point, and looked down at the beach.

They saw a boatload of swarthy Lilywhites, armed with swords and daggers and pistols and dressed in gaudy pirate gear, digging holes in the beach.

Suddenly Benito Benita leapt from one of these holes, holding up the remains of the little *Poppykettle*. The winds and waves of many long years had buried it in the sand. He held it aloft with a shout of triumph, and then shook it violently. Three brass keys fell onto the beach.

Areca knew she was beaten, although she was tempted to interfere. She thought for a moment of asking her two friends, the sympathetic crows, to swoop down onto the beach and grab the keys before the pirates could try them in the jewel boxes. But then she realised that crows never do anything without long gossip and discussion, and that there would not be time for her to go through all that kind of argument.

She watched as Benito Benita tried the keys in the boxes, with the other pirates watching eagerly. And then, as they became more and more frustrated, Areca suddenly remembered that there had been *six* brass keys. Three of them had fallen out of the *Poppykettle* when the dolphin dumped the clay pot onto the beach, and she seemed to recall that Don Avante had later buried them somewhere along the cliffs but could not remember why.

Benito Benita shouted angrily 'Each box has two locks and it needs two keys! Search for them, men!'

The pirates obeyed but they could not find the other keys. At last Benito Benita decided to bury the unopened jewel boxes, and when the other pirates asked him why he answered 'Because pirates always bury their treasure, you fools!'

He chose a spot on a hill some distance to the north-east of Limeburner's Point, and there the boxes still lie, alongside fragments of the *Poppykettle*, near a site marked today by one lonely tombstone.

CHAPTER SIX

AFTER THIS EXPERIENCE, ARECA settled in a Third People commune at a place with the Lilywhite name of Trunky Creek, in the mountains south of the thriving Lilywhite town of Bathurst. By that time many more Third People immigrants had arrived in the minds of homesick Lilywhites, and a good many had found new roles for themselves in the Unchosen Land.

Areca began to train Ludwig Wednesday, and his son Ludwig Thursday, in the science of future-telling based on Realtime information, and found them apt pupils. They had both been born in the Black Forest of Bavaria, and in appearance and outlook they were both traditional gnomes of folk-lore.

Ludwig Wednesday quickly grasped the fundamentals of future-telling and Areca thought that he might eventually make contact with the Bellringers, but Ludwig Thursday was a trifle headstrong and eccentric. However he had yet to reach his hundredth birthday and so had plenty of time to mature.

Apart from these two, Areca found that Doremifa Solati was the most interesting student in the commune. Areca guessed that she had remarkable potential but she had spent too much time in the presence of Lilywhites and had picked up many of their bad habits. She came from a library of theatre tales in Italy, and before migrating she had been the resident gnome of La Scala Opera House in Milan.

Areca often became impatient with Doremifa's materialistic thoughts, but she realised that the Third People would need liberated women to lead them as well as males and that Doremifa had leadership qualities.

Areca laid down a series of predictions concerning events that would soon effect both the Oldshadows and the Lilywhites, and worked with Arnica and the Bellringers on formulating 'specials' for the animals. Lilywhite settlement had given the animals a hard time, and they were always grateful for these 'specials' which forewarned them of Lilywhite activities affecting their lives.

One of these 'special' predictions warned that the Lilywhites would shortly mount one of their savage attacks upon the environment in the Trunky Creek region, in search of the yellow metal which they desired so avidly. Great hardship for the animals and wide devastation of their habitats would result from the gold rush, and the commune tried to help all creatures to prepare for these wounds of the future.

One dark night in 1850, after Areca had made her daily prediction to the assembled Third People, she asked Ludwig Wednesday to stay with her by the fire for a few minutes. The Third People had never known her to break the tradition of silence between prediction and sleep, and they wondered what was happening.

Quietly, Areca told Ludwig that she would soon leave the commune to live by herself. She passed the leadership of the commune into Ludwig's hands, and told him that he would perform a heavy task during the coming gold rush. He protested that he and the others were not yet ready to be left alone, but she insisted. She explained many things to him that night and she was still talking when the sun lightened the sky beyond the mountains.

Ludwig understood that Areca had become tired, and that she did not want to witness the terrible devastation that the Lilywhites would cause, but she promised that she would always be available to give advice. The two crows had promised to take care of her and they would carry messages to and fro.

As the commune began to stir from sleep she offered to answer any questions from Ludwig before she departed. He thought deeply, and then asked 'If ever I should talk directly with a Lilywhite, and he should ask me how I am able to foretell the future, what should I say?'

The two crows were gathering Areca's belongings together and were impatient to leave, but she took time to tell him 'You must repeat only the second half of the winning prediction at the great Challenge of the Black Stump, selected by the Bellringers from so many entries. No Lilywhite will ever understand it, but it runs as follows—'

> *Six for the six proud walkers*
> *Five for the symbols at your door*
> *Four for the gospel makers*
> *Three, three the rivals*
> *Two, two the Lilywhite boys dressed all in green-oh*
> *One is one and only one and evermore shall be so.*

69

Author's Note

Three years before Areca left the Trunky Commune, two men were digging for lime in the side of a cliff at Limeburners Point, near Geelong. One of their shovels clinked against metal, and they dug out two ancient keys. Nobody could understand why old keys should be buried so deep in the cliff. In that year, 1847, Lilywhites had been in Geelong only for a short time, and the Oldshadows never used metal objects of any kind.

Exactly 128 years after Areca left the commune, with her two crow companions, I met her one afternoon by some old barns at Longford, Tasmania By that time she had taken the Lilywhite name of Teresa Green. She talked about many things, and explained that the two brass keys found by the lime diggers had been buried there by Don Avante in the sixteenth century. He had actually buried three keys but only two were found. The third, she said, is now used to open secrets of The Marginal World. That is another story.